Observing Seeds

1a What do these items have in common?

1b What will they become?

2a Sort the items into two groups.

2b Explain how you sorted them.

Seeds Become Plants

1a Put an old adult-sized sock over your shoes and walk around the school field or verges.

1b Remove the socks and place each in a plastic food bag (do not seal).

1c Spray the contents with water and tape to a warm, sunny window.

2   Write what you think will happen.

_____
_____
_____
_____

3   Look at the bag for 14 days. Describe what grows.

_____
_____
_____
_____

Growing Plants

1. Which plant does each seed grow into? Draw a line to match the correct seed to its plant.

Seeds Starting to Grow

1 Write a list below of what seeds need to grow.

2a Research some fun facts on seeds. For example: Which is the biggest seed in the world? How long can seeds last? Which seed takes longest to germinate?

2b Write your fun facts below. You can add drawings if you want to.

Germination

Sow some different seeds onto damp cotton wool.

1. Make a prediction. Which seeds do you think will be the first to germinate? Give a reason for your answer.

2. Which seed do you think will germinate last? Give a reason for your answer.

3. Observe your seeds every day. Draw and label your investigation below.

Roots and Shoots

1. Look at the seeds you have germinated. Draw what you can see.

2. Use the words below to label the parts of the seedling.

    leaves, root, seed coat, shoot

3. Are the first two leaves the same or different from the other leaves that grow on the plant? Explain your answer.

Science Skills

Investigate it!

1a What is this flower called?

_____

1b What does this flower grow from?

_____

2   Create a new type of flower and draw it growing from a bulb.

   Label the parts of your new flower.

Science Skills

3 Find out the names of other flowers that grow from a bulb and list them below.

_____

_____

4 Ask an adult to help you to cut an onion in half from top to bottom. Draw and label what you can see. Use the words below to help you.

papery outer covering, roots, thick leaves

Tubers

1a Ask an adult to help you cut in half and observe (or research) a tuber. Tell a partner how it is different from the bulb you have cut in half.

_____
_____

1b Write how a tuber is the same as a bulb.

_____
_____

2 Research the names of some flowers that grow from tubers and write them below.

_____
_____

3 What are the names of some tubers we can eat?

_____
_____

Keeping Plants Healthy

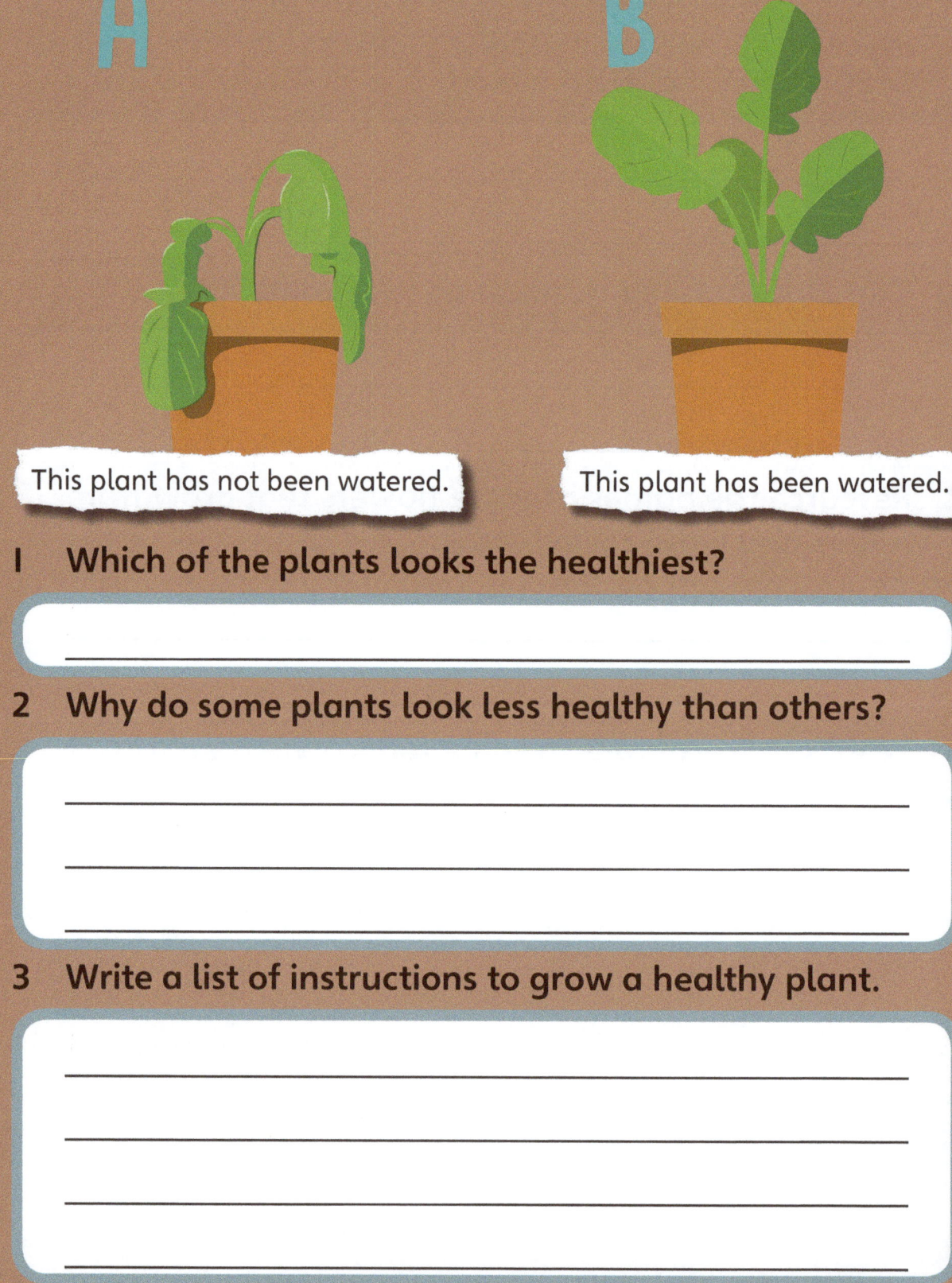

A

B

This plant has not been watered.

This plant has been watered.

1 Which of the plants looks the healthiest?

2 Why do some plants look less healthy than others?

3 Write a list of instructions to grow a healthy plant.

Science Skills

Investigate it!

1. Draw pictures to show how you think the plants will grow from the labelled pots.

2. What question you would like to investigate about growing plants?

Science Skills

Measure it!

Week	Height (cm)
1	2 cm
2	5 cm
3	10 cm

Class 2 have been growing a plant. They measured the height of the plant every week for three weeks. Their results are shown in the table

1 Draw a bar chart or pictogram to show the growth of the plant.

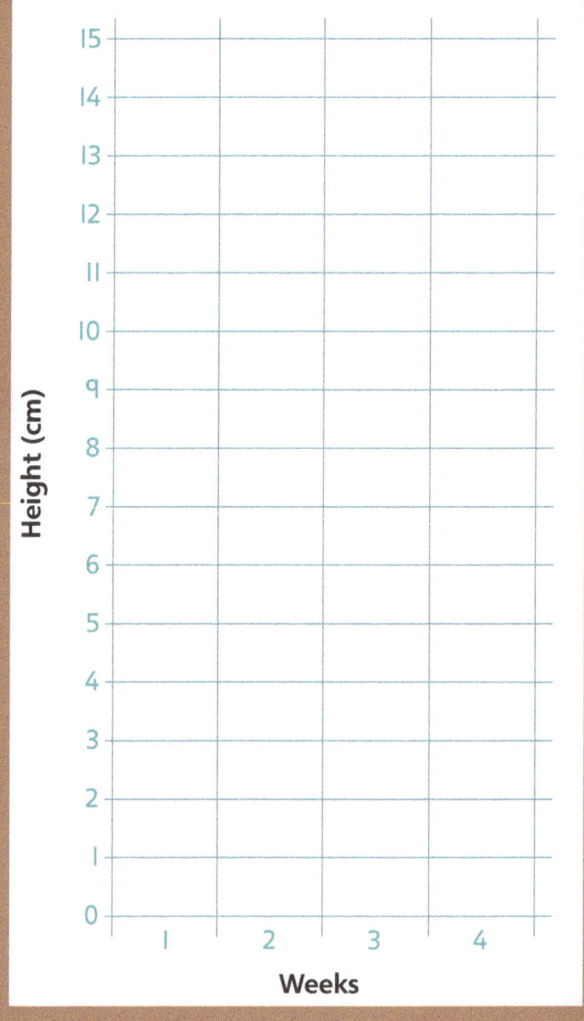

2 Draw onto your graph, how tall do you predict the plant will be in week four?

Finding Seeds

1. Where do seeds come from?

   _____
   _____
   _____

2. Ask an adult to help you to cut open some flowers, fruits and vegetables to find out if there are any seeds inside. Record your findings below.

Name of flower, fruit or vegetable	How many seeds

3. Which flower, fruit or vegetable had the most seeds?

   _____

Growing Plants

4 Which flower, fruit or vegetable had the largest seed?

_____

5 Use the results from your table to create a pictogram or bar chart below.

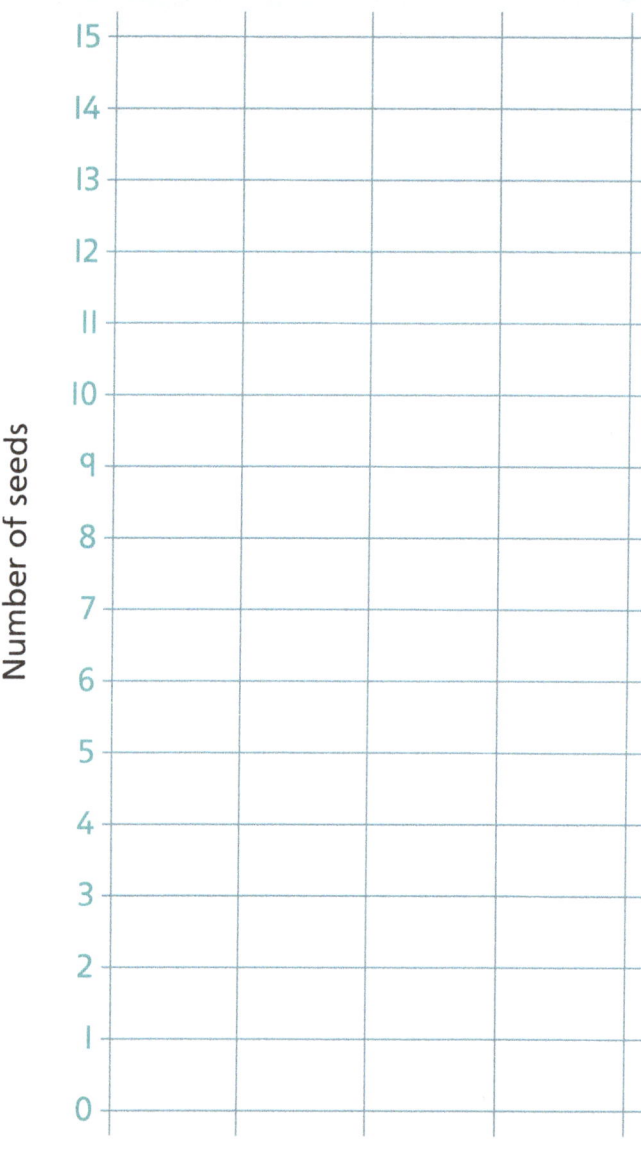

Name of flower, fruit or vegetable

Seeds You Can Eat

Some seeds are poisonous and do not taste good. Other seeds are eaten.

1. **Find out about seeds we can eat and seeds we do not eat. Make lists in the table below.**

Seeds we can eat	Seeds we cannot eat

There is a seed bank in England. It stores millions of seeds from all around the world. If a plant ever died out in nature, seeds from the bank could be grown to replace it.

2. **Which seeds do you like to eat and would you save for the future?**

What Seeds and Bulbs Need to Grow

1 In the space below, draw and label a diagram to show everything a seed or bulb needs to grow.

2 What have you learned about growing plants?

_____

_____

_____

INTERNATIONAL

Fuel curiosity, spark imagination.

| UK National Curriculum YEAR 2 | CAMBRIDGE primary Stages 1, 3 | Pearson iPRIMARY YEAR 1 |

Science Bug International is an exciting and comprehensive science programme that has been designed to make sure your children never stop asking questions about their world!

This Workbook contains questions from the Topic Book plus additional questions to reinforce and extend learning.

With full and comprehensive coverage of the skills and knowledge required for curriculum attainment, *Science Bug International* will help you to nurture and inspire your young scientist.

Series editor: Deborah Herridge
Author: Eleanor Atkinson

www.pearsonschools.co.uk
myorders@pearson.com

ISBN 978-0-435-19594-6